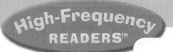

Dogs

Written by Amy Levin

Illustrated by Sue Dennen

Scholastic Inc.
New York   Toronto   London   Auckland   Sydney
Mexico City   New Delhi   Hong Kong

ISBN 0-439-13191-X

12 11 10   5/0

Printed in China   62

My dog can walk.

My dog can jump.

My dog can catch.

My dog can sleep.

My dog can sit.

My dog can swim.

We like dogs!